WOW!

WINDOW ON THE WORLD

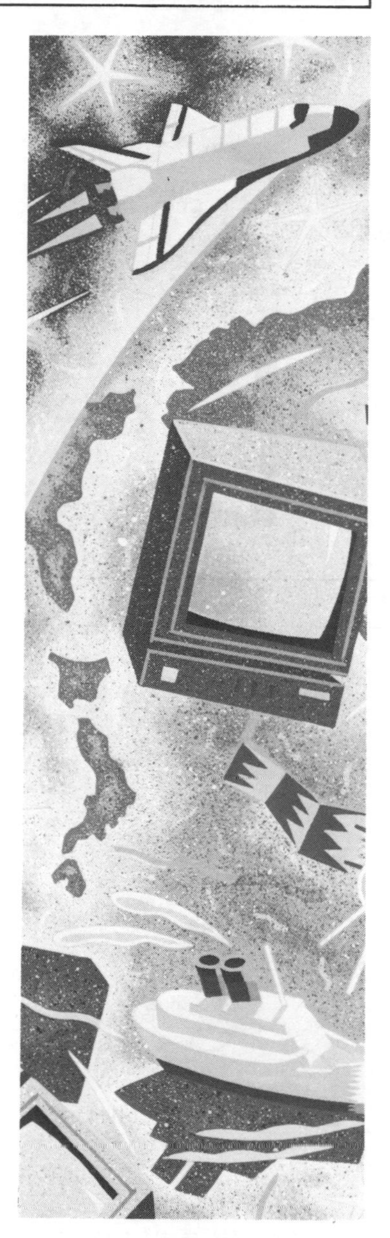

Workbook 1 • Rob Nolasco

Oxford University Press

Welcome to the *WOW!* Workbook.

A

Complete the sentences.

My first name is ....

My surname is ....

B

A *WOW!* Quiz

Write the answers.

1 What's his name?

2 What's her name?

1 He's ....

2 She's ....

Where is it?

3 C _____

4 A ______

5 A _________

6 J _____

C

Complete the sentences.

1 Tony .... from England.

2 I'm from ....

3 .... from West Germany.

4 It's from ....

5 .... from ....

6 .... from ....

D

Complete the crossword.
Write the numbers in words.

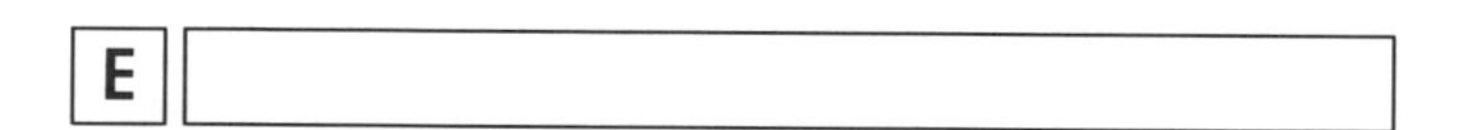

E

Write the answers.

■ Example

Is it from England?

Yes, it is.

1 Is it from China?

....

2 Is it from Africa?

....

3 Is it from South America?

....

4 Is it from the South Pole?

....

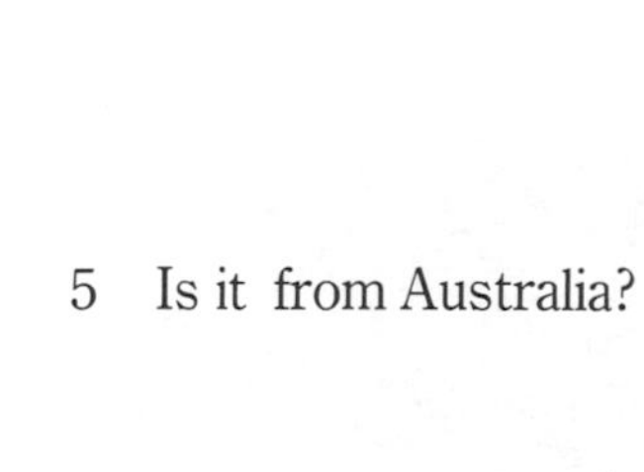

5 Is it from Australia?

....

6 Is it from Japan?

....

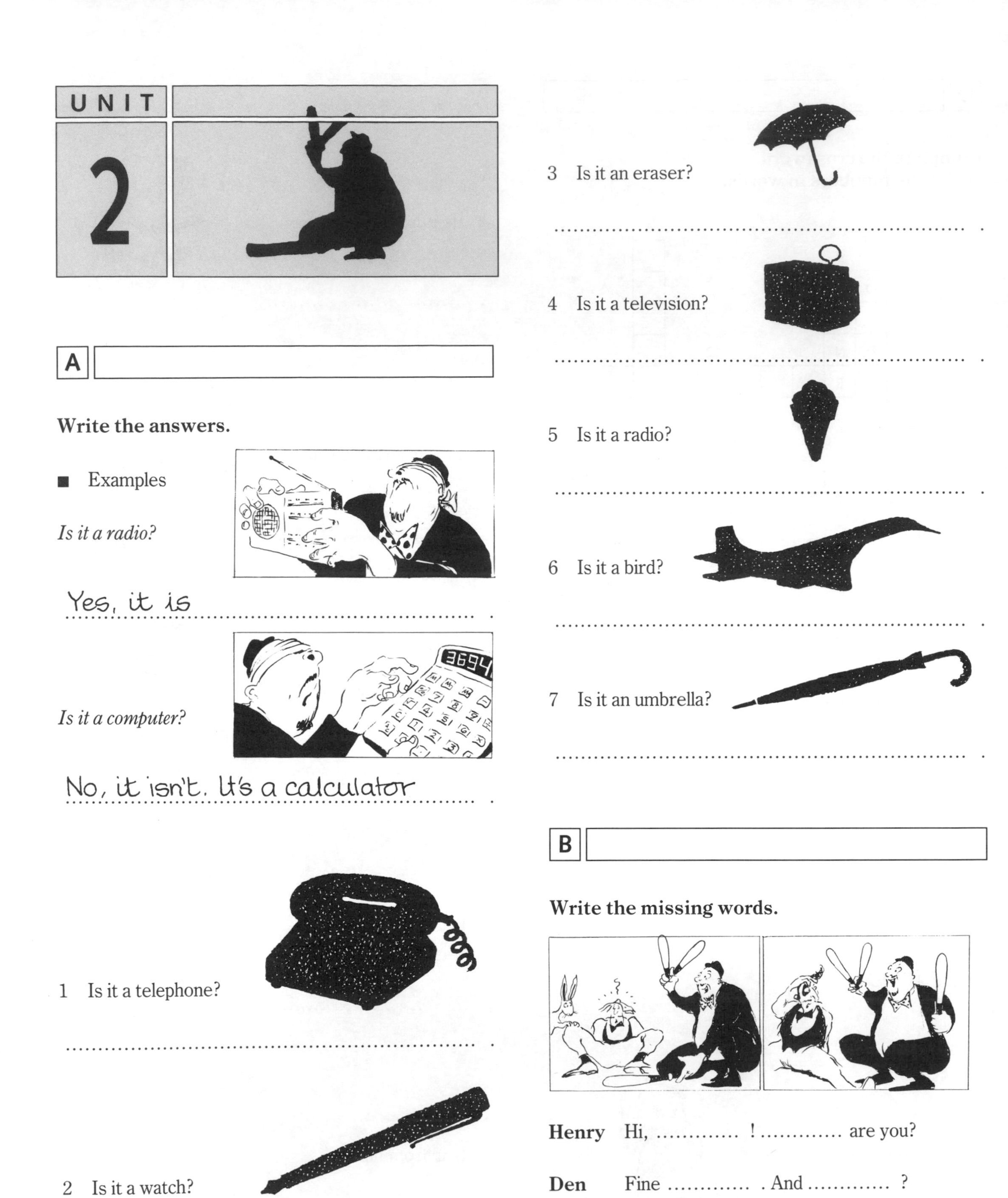

UNIT 2

A

Write the answers.

■ Examples

Is it a radio?

Yes, it is ....

Is it a computer?

No, it isn't. It's a calculator ....

1 Is it a telephone?

....

2 Is it a watch?

....

3 Is it an eraser?

....

4 Is it a television?

....

5 Is it a radio?

....

6 Is it a bird?

....

7 Is it an umbrella?

....

B

Write the missing words.

Henry Hi, ... ! .... are you?

Den Fine .... And .... ?

Henry .... fine.

C

Name the job.

■ Example

a teacher ....

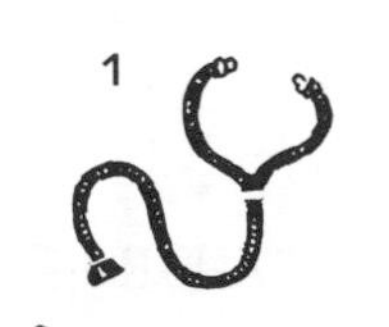

1 ....

2 ....

3 ....

4 ....

5 ....

6 ....

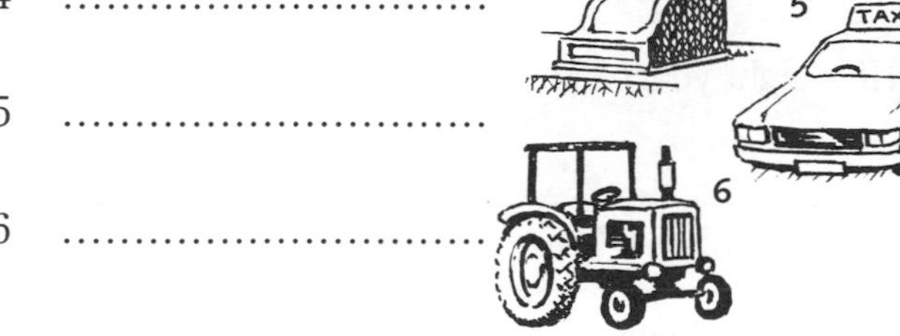

D

Name the country.

■ Example

Greece ....

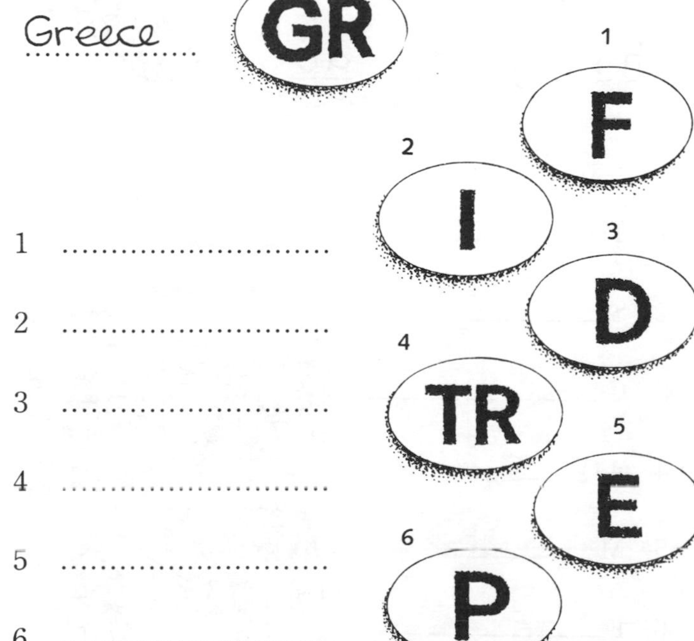

1 ....

2 ....

3 ....

4 ....

5 ....

6 ....

E

A Puzzle

Look at Henry's notebook.
Write the answers.

a = 1............

b = 3............

c = ...

d = ...

e = ...

f = ...

g = ...

h = ...

i = ...

Write the phone numbers.

1 b c e g g i a

The number is three ....

....

2 a h i f f c d

The number is six ....

....

EXTRA! EXTRA!

A

Complete the sentences.

1 What .... it?

2 I think ....

3 .... this?

4 I think ....

5 .... it an umbrella?

6 No, I think ....

B

Write the questions.

Nellie Chi-Chi

■ Example

What's her name? ....

Her name's Nellie.

1 .... ?

She's one year old.

2 .... ?

She's from Africa.

3 .... ?

A-F-R-I-C-A.

4 .... ?

His name's Chi-chi.

5 .... ?

He's eight years old.

6 .... ?

He's from China.

C

What's on TV?

■ Example

Things to do

1 The N_ _ _ _

2 S_ _ _ _ _

3 C_ _ _ _ _ _ _ _ _

4 A Q_ _ _ _

5 M_ _ _ _ _

6 F_ _ _ _ _ _ _ _

WORDPOWER

A

Find six countries in the word square.

C	I	T	A	L	Y	G
A	S	U	J	I	E	R
N	F	R	A	N	C	E
A	U	K	P	O	H	E
D	N	E	A	D	I	C
A	E	Y	N	A	N	E
S	P	A	I	N	A	D

B

Put the words in alphabetical order.

eraser umbrella ruler television map
artist aeroplane watch student teacher

1 aeroplane ....
2 artist ....
3 ....
4 ....
5 ....
6 ....
7 ....
8 ....
9 ....
10 ....

C

Find seven words from these letters.

n e f x i f v s e n t

Write the words in column A.
Write the number in column B.

	A	B
1	five	5
2	s_ _	....
3	t_ _	....
4	s_ _ _ _	....
5	f_ _ _ _ _ _ _	....
6	s_ _ _ _ _ _ _ _ _ _	....
7	n_ _ _	....

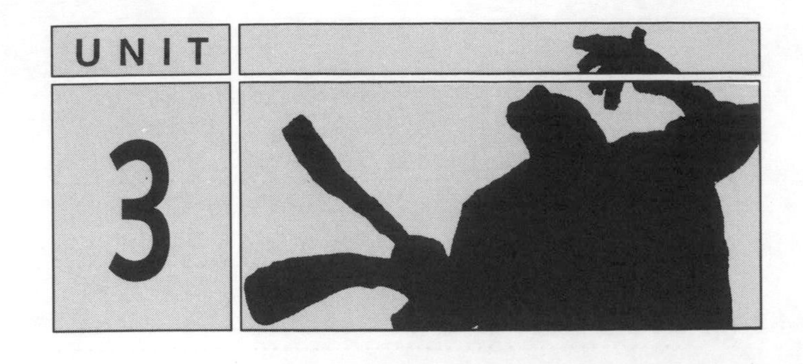

A

Make eight true sentences.

■ Examples

I've got an eraser .

I haven't got a television. .

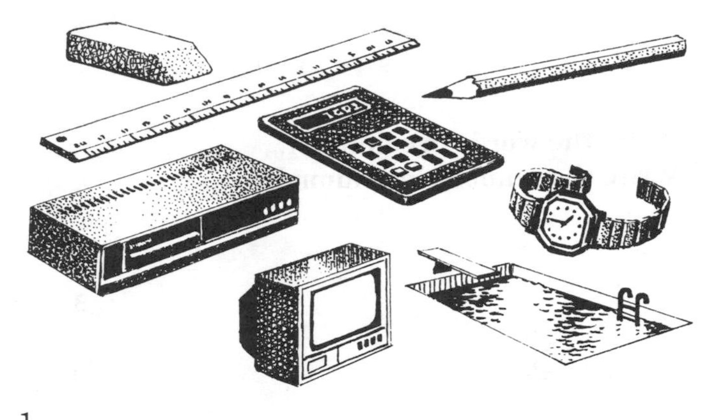

1 ....

2 ....

3 ....

4 ....

5 ....

6 ....

7 ....

8 ....

B

Write questions about the hotel and the rooms.

■ Example

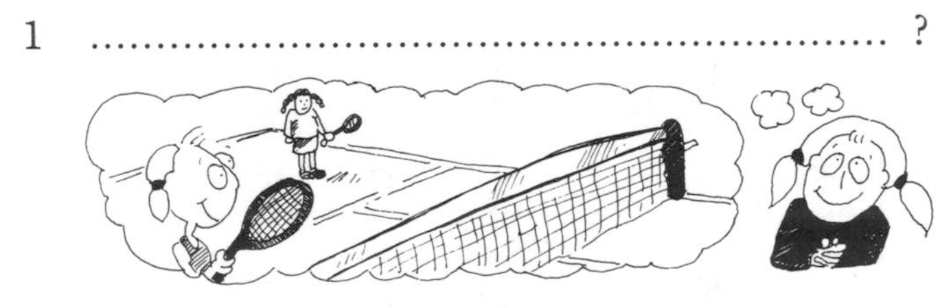

1 .... ?

2 .... ?

3 .... ?

4 .... ?

5 .... ?

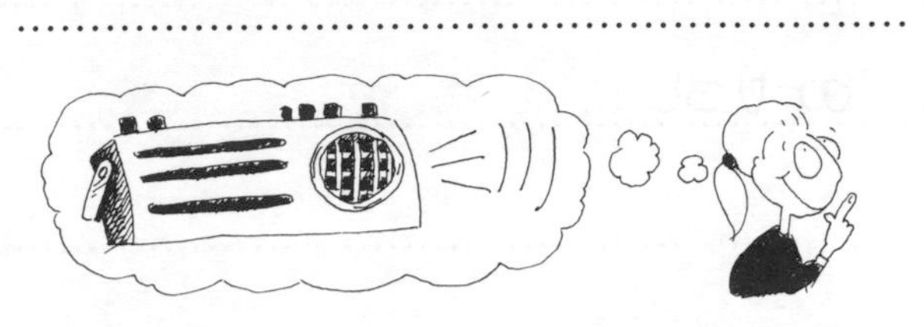

6 .... ?

C

Complete the sentences. Use *this* or *that*.

■ Example

This *is a book.*

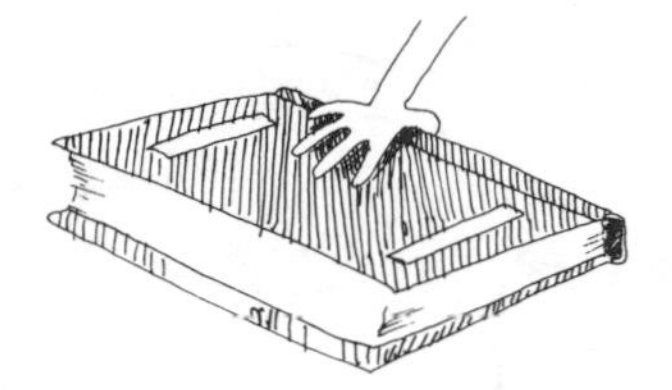

1 Is .... a bird?

2 Is .... a book or a notebook?

3 Who's ....?

4 What's ....?

5 .... is Sherlock Holmes.

6 .... is Dominic.

D

Match the numbers with the words.

1	57	a	seventy-five
2	90	b	sixty-three
3	88	c	nineteen
4	47	d	twenty-five
5	63	e	fifty-seven
6	74	f	eighty-eight
7	25	g	forty-seven
8	75	h	thirty-six
9	36	i	seventy-four
10	19	j	ninety

■ Example *1* = e............

2 = ... 7 = ...

3 = ... 8 = ...

4 = ... 9 = ...

5 = ... 10 = ...

6 = ...

UNIT 4

A

Write sentences with *this* or *these*.

■ Example

Satomi

This is Satomi's ....

Helen

1 ....

Barry

2 ....

Tony

3 ....

Shirley

4 ....

Maradona

5 ....

Batman

6 ....

B

Complete the conversation.

Have you got the time, please?

No, I'm sorry. I .... got a watch.

Have you got .... ?

Excuse me, have .... a watch?

No, why?

What time .... !?

It's ....

C

Write in the times. ■ Example *In London it's twelve o'clock. In Athens it's* two o'clock. . .

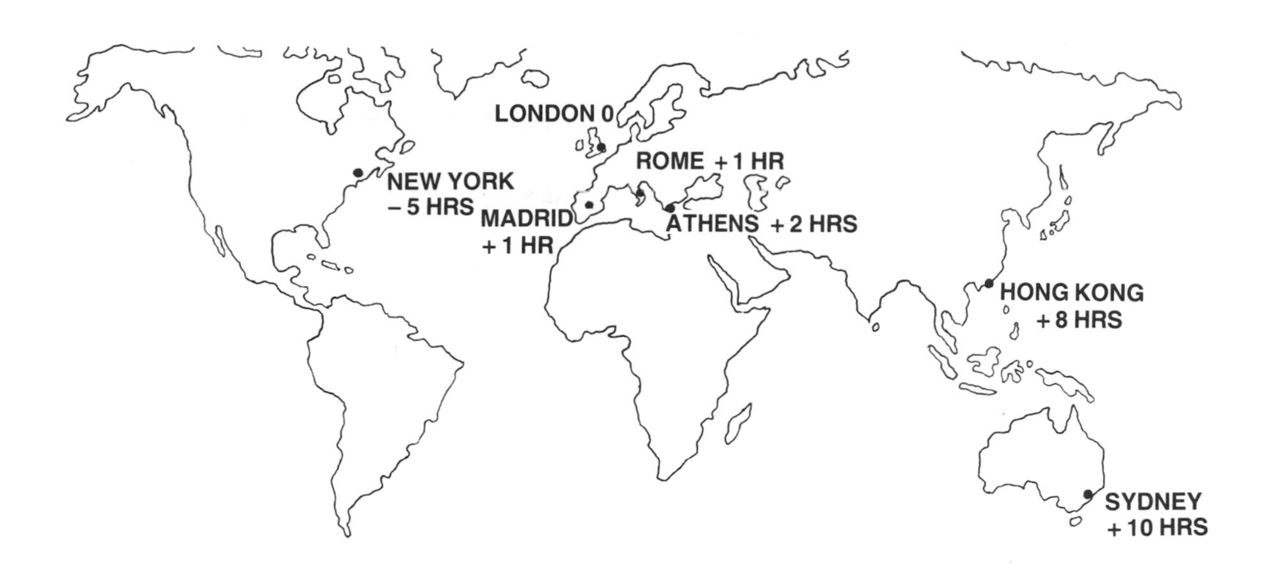

1 In London it's ten o'clock. In Athens it's

....

2 In London it's twelve o'clock. In New York it's

....

3 In Rome it's three o'clock. In London it's

....

4 In London it's twelve o'clock. In Hong Kong it's

....

5 In London it's one o'clock. In Sydney it's

....

6 In Madrid it's seven o'clock. In London it's

....

D

Answer these questions and complete this card to Shirley.

Dear Shirley,

Please, can I join the WOW club?

1 What is your name? My name...
2 How old are you? I am...
3 What is your address? My address...
4 What class are you in? I'm in...
5 What is the name of your English teacher?
My English teacher...

EXTRA! EXTRA!

A

Find six colours.

G B L U E R

G R E Y G E

L O N P R D

T W H I T E

B N O N E W

B E C K O N

1 .... 4 ....

2 .... 5 ....

3 .... 6 ....

B

Draw your family tree.

HENRY = ANGELA

ALAN NICK LAURA = JO

HENRY

C

Complete the sentences. Use these words.

grandfather uncle daughter son aunt

sister grandmother

■ Example

Your mother's sister is your aunt .

1 Your mother's sister is your

....

2 Your father's father is your

....

3 Your father's brother is your

....

4 Your aunt is your father's

....

5 Your mother's mother is your

....

6 Your brother is your mother's

....

7 Your sister is your mother's

....

WORDPOWER

A

Put a word in each space. Use these words.

book *case* *passport* *photograph*
ticket *timetable*

1 Peter's ....

2 Howard's ....

3 Peter's ....

4 Sally's ....

5 Peter's ....

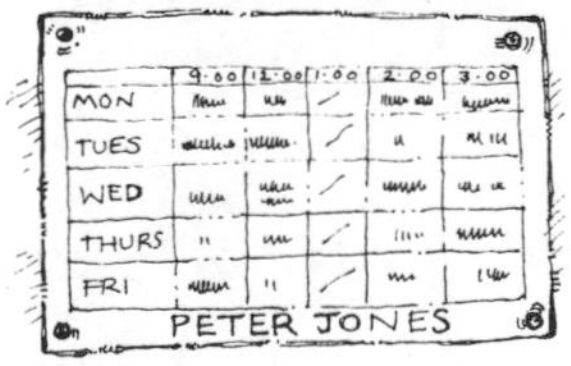

6 Kim's ....

B

Make words from these letters.

e d o r o m b

1 ....

o a r h o m t b

2 ....

n h i t k c e

3 ....

s c r o l a s m o

4 ....

o p h t s i l a

5 ....

a e t a r s n u r t

6 ....

C

Put the words in alphabetical order.

swimming-pool sister sweater
summer student sky six spring
special speaking

sister, six, ...

....

....

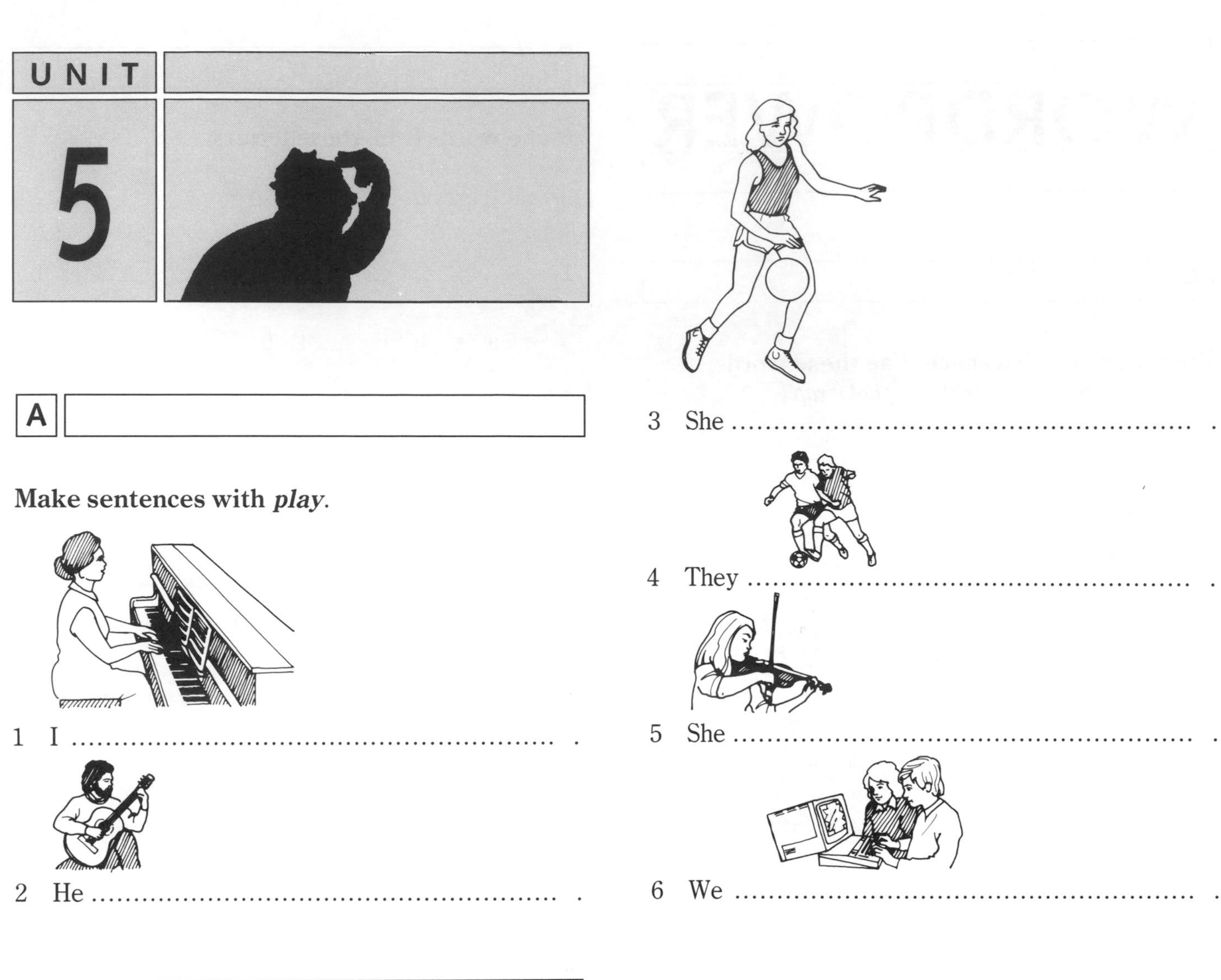

Make sentences with *play*.

1 I ....

2 He ....

3 She ....

4 They ....

5 She ....

6 We ....

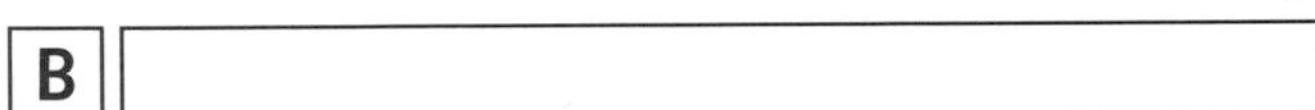

Write about Henry's day and your day.

■ Example		Henry's day		My day
have dinner		Henry has dinner at 10 p.m.		I have dinner at 8 p.m.
get up	1	....	2	....
have lunch	3	....	4	....
go to bed	5	....	6	....

C

Complete the table for you and a partner. Make true sentences.

	1	2	3	4	5
Henry	✓	✓	✗	✓	✗
Me	.....	.....	.....	.....	.....
My partner	.....	.....	.....	.....	.....

Henry

1 He plays the piano .

2 He plays the guitar .

3 He ....

4 He ....

5 He ....

Me

1 I ....

2 I ....

3 I ....

4 I ....

5 I ....

My partner

1 My partner ....

2 My partner ....

3 My partner ....

4 My partner ....

5 My partner ....

D

Complete the text with these verbs.

goes *don't watch* *wants* *have got*
learn *do* *play* *is* *live*

Mike Hall[1]............ to be a footballer.

He [2]............ to Lilleshall.

Lilleshall [3]............ a special school.

The students [4]............ in Lilleshall.

In the morning they [5]............ normal lessons.

In the afternoon they [6]............ to play football!!

On weekday evenings, Mike and his friends [7]............ television, they [8]............ their homework. And every Saturday, they [9]............ a match!!

UNIT

6

A

Write the questions.

■ Example

Do you get pocket-money ?

1 I buy bubble-gum.

.... ?

2 I read comics.

.... ?

3 I buy ice-creams.

.... ?

4 I don't have a part-time job.

.... ?

5 I spend money on fizzy drinks.

.... ?

6 I don't save money.

.... ?

B

Answer the questions in Exercise A.
Use *Yes, I do.* or *No, I don't.*

■ Example

Do you get pocket-money?

No, I don't.

C

1 **Put things you like into column A and things you don't like into column B.**

pop music computer games football
basketball school classical music
chewing-gum sweets dancing
Mathematics English homework

A	B
I like	I don't like ....
....	....
....	....
....	....
....	....
....	....
....	....

2 **Make three sentences with *I like.***

■ Example

I like pop music .

....

....

....

3 **Make three sentences with *I love.***

■ Example

I love football.

....

....

....

4 **Make three sentences with *I don't like.***

....

....

....

5 **Make three sentences with *I hate.***

....

....

....

D

Write six questions to ask a partner.

■ Example

Do you listen to music?

1 .... ?

2 .... ?

3 .... ?

4 .... ?

5 .... ?

6 .... ?

EXTRA! EXTRA!

A

Put these words in the right order to make sentences.

HELEN ALWAYS DOES HOMEWORK AT HER SCHOOL

1 her | Helen | homework | always | does | at school .

....

2 special | lessons | never | she | has .

....

3 goes | swimming | she | sometimes | at the weekend .

....

4 comics | usually | she | reads .

....

5 goes | special | Robert | a | school | to .

....

6 basketball | usually | on | Sunday | he | plays .

....

B

What language is it?

■ Example ...I love you. English...

1 Je t'aime. ....

3 Ich liebe dich. ....

2 Te quiero. ....

4 Seni seviyorum. ....

C

Complete this *WOW!* profile.

My name is ....

My address is ....

....

I speak ....

I watch .... on television.

I like ....

I don't like ....

Now do a profile for a friend.

Her/his name is ....

Her/his address is ....

....

....

....

....

WORDPOWER

A

Write the words.

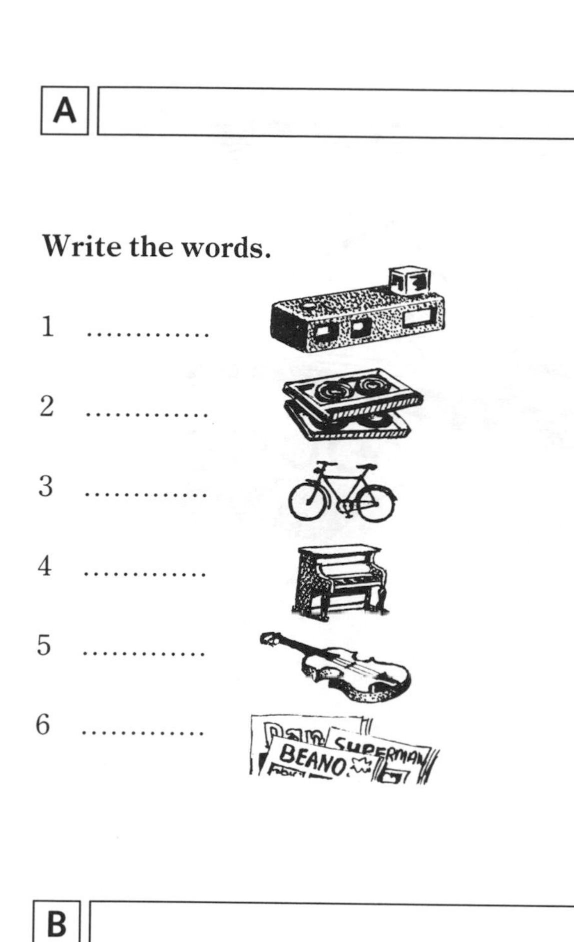

1 ....

2 ....

3 ....

4 ....

5 ....

6 ....

B

Match the verbs to the pictures.

1 .... a buy

2 .... b sing

3 .... c collect stamps

4 .... d dance

5 .... e listen

6 .... f read

C

What time does Henry eat?
Use these words to complete Henry's sentence.

lunch *snacks* *breakfast* *dinner*

I have .... at 11.00 a.m., ... at 3.00 p.m. and .... at 10.00 p.m. *and* I eat .... all day!!

Now write a sentence about the times you eat.

....

....

D

Do you buy these with your pocket-money?
Write the words.

■ Example
estsew ....sweets....

1 mbubgbleu ....

2 ridnsk ....

3 ciumghewng ....

4 scastsctc ....

5 slcohet ....

6 mesga ....

A

Safety at the beach

Put in the correct form of these verbs.

go *throw* *swim* *wear* *use*

■ Example

Always swim *with a friend.* Don't go *swimming alone.*

1 .... far from the beach.

2 Never .... after a big meal.

3 .... a hat if the sun is hot.

4 .... sun-cream.

5 .... litter on the beach.

6 .... near windsurfers.

B

Write the conversation.
Put in the capital letters and the spaces between words.

oh!den.iwantarideonyourwindsurfer,please.sure,hereyouare.thanks!butbecareful!don'tgoneartheswimmers!don'tworry!idon'tlikewater.iwantarideonthebeach!

Henry Oh! Den. ....

....

Den ....

Henry ....

Den ....

Henry ....

C

Complete the sentences with *mine, ours, his, hers, yours, theirs.*

■ Example

Is that Henry's? *Yes, it's* his ....

1 Is this your book? Yes, it's ....

2 Is that Helen's? Yes, it's ....

3 Are they Nick's? Yes, they're ....

4 Are these his? No they're ....
We've got three.

5 Whose record is it? I think it's ....
They like Michael Jackson.

6 Is the T-shirt ....? No, it isn't mine.

D

Match the expressions in column A with the responses in column B.

	A		B
1	Hello!	a	Never mind. We've got time!
2	Be careful!	b	Thanks!
3	I'm very sorry!	c	Don't worry.
4	I'm sorry I'm late.	d	Hi!
5	Here you are!	e	It doesn't matter!

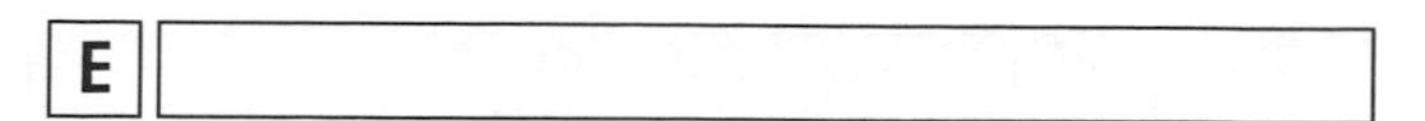

E

Complete the sentences.

■ Example

UNIT 8

A

Complete the questions for these answers.

■ Example

What 's your name ?

My name's Shirley.

1 Where .... ?

I'm from Canada.

2 Where .... ?

I live in London.

3 What time .... ?

I get up at seven o'clock.

4 What .... ?

I hate football.

5 Why .... ?

I hate football because it's boring.

6 What .... ?

I like listening to music.

B

What does Henry hate doing? Write sentences.

■ Example

get up

He hates getting up.

clean the house

1 ....

listen to classical music

2 ....

swim

3 ....

play computer games

4 ....

run

5 ....

shop

6 ....

C

Make true sentences for you and a partner. Use the verb + *-ing*.

■ Example

I love watching WOW! .

1 I like ....

2 I hate ....

3 I love ....

4 My partner likes ....

5 My partner hates ....

6 My partner loves ....

D

Answer the questions to write a short paragraph about young people in your country.

What clothes do young people like?
What are their hobbies?
What do they think of school?
What subjects do they like?

■ Example

Young people in Britain like T-shirts,...

They ride bicycles,...

....

....

....

....

....

EXTRA! EXTRA!

A

Use the table to make six questions.

■ Example

How often does she play basketball?

Where Why Which What How often What time	do does	they you she/he	hate? play basketball? like? go to school? tidy your room? go to the cinema?

1 .... ?

2 .... ?

3 .... ?

4 .... ?

5 .... ?

6 .... ?

B

Write the numbers in words.

1 1,001 ....

2 369 ....

3 1,400 ....

4 1,450 ....

5 30,300 ....

6 200,000 ....

7 3,000,000 ....

C

Write the missing words.

1st	first	6th	....
2nd	....	7th	....
3rd	....	8th	....
4th	fourth	9th	....
5th	....	10th	....

D

Write the answers.

■ Example *Add one to one hundred. Answer:* 101

1 Multiply two hundred by five. Answer: ....

2 Subtract two hundred and fifty from a thousand.

Answer: ....

3 Divide twenty thousand by four.

Answer: ....

4 Add one hundred thousand to nine hundred thousand and one.

Answer: ....

5 Subtract two hundred from one thousand two hundred.

Answer: ....

6 Multiply this number by fifty. Answer: ....

WORDPOWER

A

Do you wear these?
Write the words.

■ Example

hirsts-T T-shirts

1 njeas ....

2 kcartsitus ....

3 wearets ....

4 ingraitn shseo ....

5 toosb ....

6 ahts ....

B

Match the words to the definitions.

	Words		Definitions
1	Sunday	a	The tenth month of the year.
2	Tuesday	b	The third day of the week.
3	October	c	The first day of the week.
4	Thursday	d	Next after the first.
5	weekend	e	The fourth month of the year.
6	April	f	Saturday and Sunday.
7	second	g	The fifth day of the week.

■ Example

1 Sunday c The first day of the week.

C

Hobbies

Write the names of the hobbies.

■ Example

chess

1 ....

2 ....

3 ....

4 ....

5 ....

6 ....

D

Put in the missing words.

I go to the b e a c h in s _ _ _ _ _ _ .

I sit and read my c _ _ _ _ but I don't

b _ _ _ because I use s _ _ - _ _ _ _ _ _

and I take an u _ _ _ _ _ _ _ _ .

UNIT 9

A

Describe the way out.
Use *through, under, over, up, down.*

You go

1 down a wall   3 .... a fence   5 .... a wall

2 .... the tunnel   4 .... the rope   6 .... the rope.

B

Look at this picture and answer the questions.

■ Example

Is there a tennis court? Yes, there is .

1 Is there a swimming-pool? ....

2 Is there a restaurant? ....

3 Are there any computers? ....

4 Is there a gymnasium? ....

5 Are there any shops? ....

6 Is there an art room? ....

7 Are there any BMX-bikes? ....

C

Look at the picture in B and make six sentences. Use *there is* or *there are.*

■ Example

There is a tennis-court .

D

Find six verbs.

C	B	S	T	J	A	Z
L	R	T	R	U	N	S
I	A	A	E	M	P	W
M	K	N	W	P	O	I
B	Y	D	N	L	D	M

Match a verb to a picture.

■ Example

run

1 ....

2 ....

3 ....

4 ....

5 ....

UNIT 10

A

Read this text.

Tanaka is an American from Hawaii.
He works in Japan.
He eats 400 kg of meat each year.
He loves pasta.
Sometimes he eats five or six plates of pasta each day.
His favourite drink is Coke.
He drinks five cans of Coke every meal.

Answer these questions.

1 Is Tanaka Japanese? ....

....

2 Where is he from? ....

....

3 Does he like meat? ....

....

4 Does he like pasta? ....

....

5 What does he drink? ....

....

Now write four more questions about Tanaka. Use *how much* or *how many.*

■ Example

How much meat does he eat each year?

How many kilos of meat does he eat each year?

6 .... ?

7 .... ?

8 .... ?

9 .... ?

B

Make a questionnaire about the food and drink in the picture.
Choose six items.

■ Example

How many slices of bread do you eat each day?

My food questionnaire

1 .... ?

2 .... ?

3 .... ?

4 .... ?

5 .... ?

6 .... ?

C

Ask someone in your family the questions in B.

■ Example

My sister's *answers.*

1 She eats three slices of bread each day.

2 She drinks...

1 ....

2 ....

3 ....

4 ....

5 ....

6 ....

D

Complete the questions.

■ Example

What time *does the train leave?*

Three o'clock.

1 How .... is the chewing-gum?

Thirty pence.

2 How .... is the bike?

About twenty years old.

3 What .... do you get up?

Six o'clock.

4 How .... is it to Japan?

Two thousand kilometres.

5 How .... rocks do you have?

Hundreds.

6 What .... are you in?

I'm in Class 4.

EXTRA! EXTRA!

A

Wordchain

Find six plural words.
List the singular forms.

quizzesboywomenmanchildrennumberspeopleice-creampencilsschool

	Plural	Singular		Plural	Singular
1	quizzes	quiz	4	....	....
2	....	....	5	....	....
3	....	....	6	....	....

B

Complete the questions.

■ Example

How *do you travel to work?*

I go by bus.

1 .... time do you spend watching television each day?

About three hours.

2 .... you swim?

No, I don't.

3 .... you ride a bike?

No, I don't.

4 .... exercise do you have each day?

Not much.

5 .... ice-creams do you eat every week?

Seven – one every day!

6 .... you fit?

No, I'm not!

C

Now you answer the questions in B.

My answers

1 ....

2 ....

3 ....

4 ....

5 ....

6 ....

WORDPOWER

A

Crossword

Across

1 A _ _ _ _ _ _ of cheese. 

2 A _ _ _ _ _ _ _ of orange juice.

3 A _ _ _ _ _ _ _ of milk. 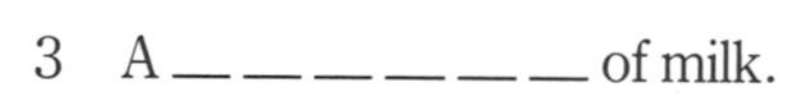

4 A _ _ _ _ _ _ of bread. 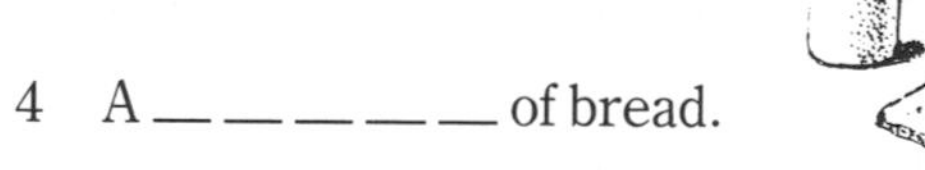

Down

1 A _ _ _ _ _ _ _ of cornflakes.

6 A _ _ _ of soup.

7 Two _ _ _ _ _ _ _ of bread. 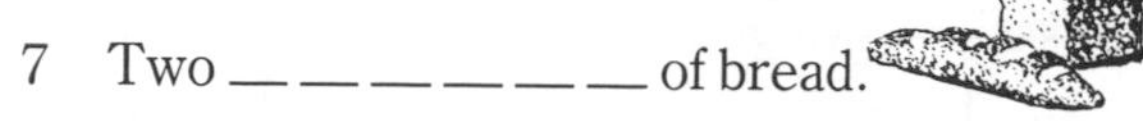

8 A _ _ _ of eggs. 

B

Look at these pictures.
Complete the sentences.

1 Picture .... shows a close encounter of the .... kind.

2 Picture .... shows .... of the .... kind.

3 Picture .... a close encounter of the ....

4 Picture ....

C

The *WOW!* holiday camp
Make words from these letters.

1 ouhse house

2 sketallba rtocu ....

3 spoh ....

4 kale ....

5 rhsocs ....

6 esrauntrta ....

UNIT 11

A

**There's something wrong with Tony's sentences.
Correct them.**

■ Example

Nick is wearing jeans ....

1 'He's doing his hair.'

....

2 'She's wearing a black skirt.'

....

3 'He's wearing a new jacket.'

....

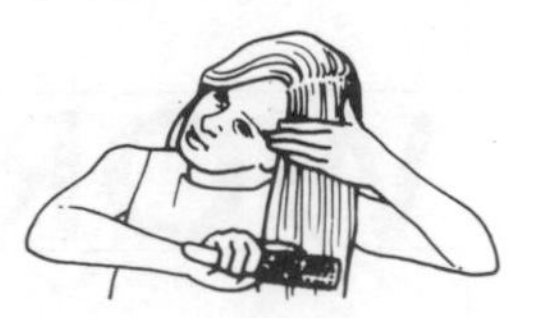

4 'She's putting on her trousers.'

....

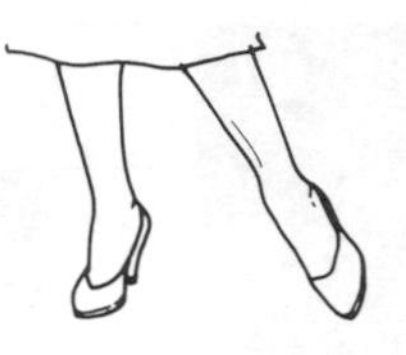

5 'She's wearing boots.'

....

6 'She's wearing a bracelet.'

....

B

**Write the *-ing* form for these verbs.
Be careful!**

	verb	*-ing* form		verb	*-ing* form
1	wear	wearing	6	listen	....
2	do	....	7	write	....
3	try	....	8	sit	....
4	shop	....	9	run	....
5	learn	....	10	make	....

C

What are they wearing?

Colour the pictures and describe what they are wearing.

■ Example

She's wearing a white T-shirt...

She's wearing ....

....

....

He's wearing ....

....

....

D

Complete these sentences with the correct form of the verb.

Use these verbs:

do listen paint play read sit watch work write

1 What .... you .... ?

I .... TV.

2 Who .... you .... to?

Michael Jackson.

3 .... they .... ?

No, they .... comics.

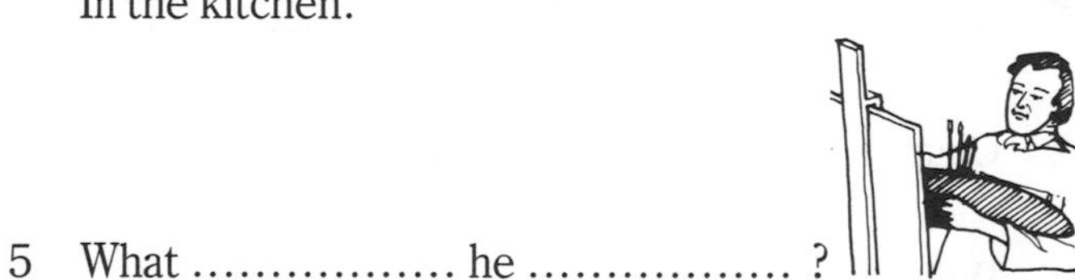

4 Where .... he .... ?

In the kitchen.

5 What .... he .... ?

6 Who .... she .... to?

7 Which teams .... ?

UNIT

12

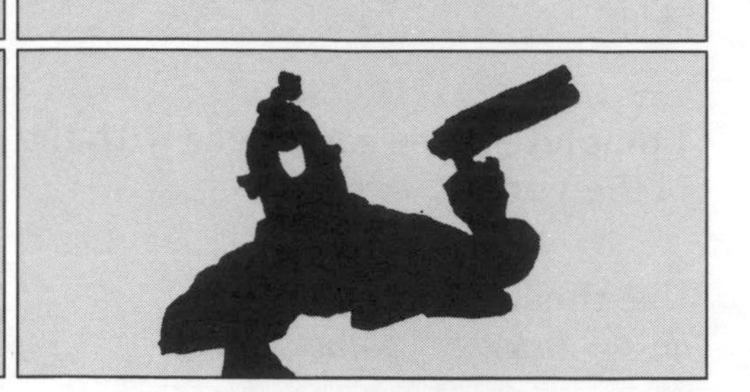

A

Communication

Use the pictures to complete the sentences about how humans and animals can communicate.

1 Humans ....can use their.... hands.

2 Chimps .... sign language.

3 Whales .... sound.

4 .... bodies.

5 .... ears and mouth.

6 .... smell.

7 .... faces.

B

Read this text.

Orcinus Orca is the killer whale. A killer whale can swim at 20 k.p.h. but it cannot see more than 30 metres. So how do killer whales find food? The answer is that they use sounds. Killer whales can hear sounds that humans cannot hear and they use sound to find food. They also use sounds to 'talk' and their sounds can travel through the water.

Now use these words to make questions.

■ Example
Can/see more than 30 metres?

....Can a killer whale see more than 30 metres.... ?

1 Can/swim at 40 k.p.h.?

.... ?

2 Can/use sounds?

.... ?

3 Can/hear sounds that we cannot?

.... ?

4 Can/use sounds to communicate?

.... ?

5 Can/find food with sounds?

.... ?

6 Can/talk through the water?

.... ?

C

Answer the questions in exercise B.

■ Example
Can a killer whale see more than 30 metres?

No, it can't. ....

1 ....

2 ....

3 ....

4 ....

5 ....

6 ....

D

Use the words to make a complete conversation.

■ Example

What is it?

I'm hungry. *Eat this.*

Thanks.

Den What is it? ....

Henry I'm hungry. ....

Den Eat this. ....

Henry Thanks. ....

1 I'm frightened.

What's the matter? I can't sleep.

Why not?

Den ....

Henry ....

Den ....

Henry ....

2 I can't see.

What's up? Why not?

I haven't got my glasses.

Den ....

Henry ....

Den ....

Henry ....

3 Thanks!

What is it? Here you are.

Have you got a pen, please?

Den ....

Henry ....

Den ....

Henry ....

EXTRA! EXTRA!

A

What are they doing?
Write a question for each picture.

1 Is he carrying a box ?

2 .... ?

3 .... ?

4 .... ?

5 .... ?

6 .... ?

7 .... ?

B

Replace the words in italic with *it* or *them*.

■ Example

Take *your bracelet* off.

Take it off.

1 Put *your hat* on.

....

2 Take *your shoes* off.

....

3 Try *the jacket* on.

....

4 Put *the trousers* here.

....

5 Buy *that new dress*.

....

6 Don't wear *your boots* in class.

....

WORDPOWER

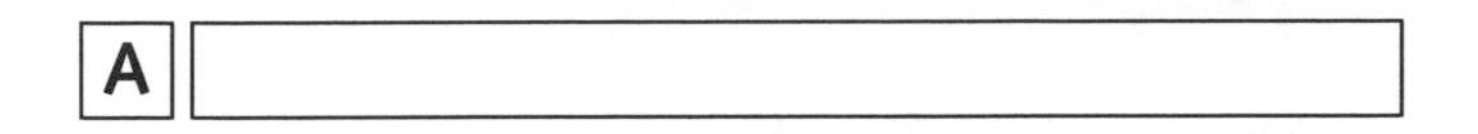

A

Complete the words and find the missing word.

1 b _ _ [_]

2 o _ _ [_] _ _ _ _ _

3 c _ [_] _ _ _ _ _ _ _ _ _

4 b _ _ [_] _ _ _ _ _

5 s [_] _ _ _

6 g _ _ _ _ _ [_]

7 t _ _ [_] _ _ _ _ _

8 e _ _ _ _ [_] _ _ _ _

9 s _ _ _ _ [_]

B

Label the diagram with these words.

face *eyes* *ears* *mouth* *hands*
head *arm* *leg* *foot*

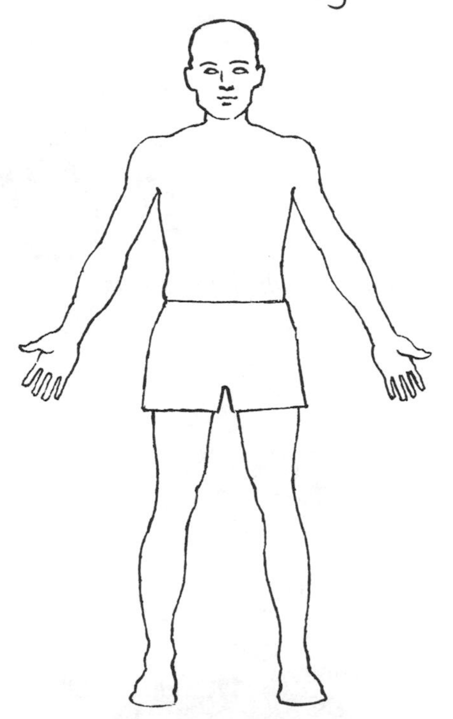

C

Put these words into the sentences.

code *communicate* *voice* *messages*
language

1 BASIC is a computer ....

2 Some computers can imitate the human ....

3 Many computers can .... by telephone.

4 Computers can send .... across the world.

5 Some computers use a ....

UNIT

13

A

Tell Henry what he must do.
Use these verbs.

brush *feed* *train* *take it for a walk*

1 It's hungry.

You must feed it .

2 Its hair is dirty.

....

3 It bites!

....

4 It sleeps all day and never goes out.

....

B

Tell the students what they mustn't do in class.

1 You mustn't chew gum .

2 ....

3 ....

4 ....

5 ....

6 ....

7 ....

C

Write the rules for this race.
Use *must go* or *mustn't go*.

1 Pipe
√

2 Fence
√
×

3 Nets
√

4 Water
√
×

5 Wall
√
×

6 Rope
√

1 ....

2 ....

....

3 ....

4 You must go round the water.

You mustn't go through it.

5 ....

....

6 ....

UNIT 14

A

Henry's diary

Here is Henry's diary for next week. Write down what he's doing on each day.

MONDAY	Fly to Paris 7 p.m.
TUESDAY	Visit the Eiffel Tower 2 p.m.
WEDNESDAY	Make a record with Den 9 a.m.
THURSDAY	Have dinner with the Boss 8 p.m.
FRIDAY	Fly home 7 a.m.
SATURDAY	Do nothing!
SUNDAY	Have a rest!

1 He's flying to Paris on Monday evening.

2 ....

3 ....

4 ....

5 ....

6 ....

7 ....

B

My plans for next week

Write seven different sentences about your plans for next week.

■ Example

I'm playing basketball on Sunday

1 ....

2 ....

3 ....

4 ....

5 ....

6 ....

7 ....

C

What are they saying?
Use *can* to complete the speech bubbles.

1 Can I borrow your pen, please ?

2 .... ?

3 .... ?

4 .... ?

5 .... ?

6 .... ?

D

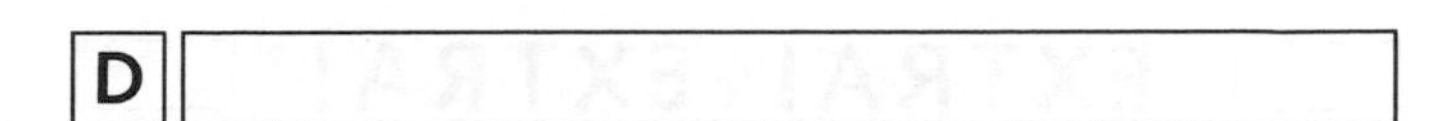

Put these sentences in the correct order to make a telephone conversation.

1 Hello, 217217.

2 ....

3 ....

4 ....

5 ....

6 ....

7 ....

8 ....

EXTRA! EXTRA!

A

Complete this text. Use *must* or *mustn't* + one of the following verbs.

worry *take* *eat (×2)* *smoke* *exercise*

Do you want to be fit? You do? Follow these simple rules.

You [1] must take exercise. Swimming, jogging, even disco dancing are good for you but you [2]............ .... for at least twenty minutes a week!

Be careful with the food you eat. If you are fat you [3]............ .... foods like sugar and chocolate. You [4]............ .... fruit and vegetables!!

Smoking is bad for you. You [5]............ ....!

Finally, you [6]............ .... Worrying makes you tired.

B

Write down what these people are doing for their next holiday.

1 She's going by Concorde to New York .

2 ....

FRANCE

3 ....

4 ....

SOLAR VILLAGE

5 ....

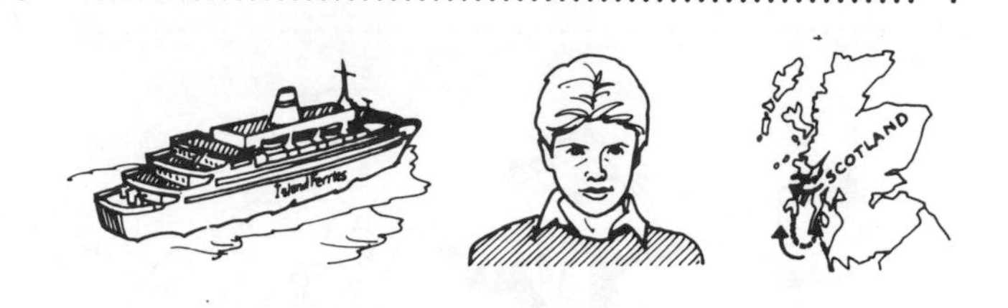

6 ....

WORDPOWER

A

Write Henry's shopping list.

Food

1 ablesgteve vegetables

2 sechee ....

3 shif ....

4 nchceik ....

5 kesca ....

6 lheoatcoc ....

7 spata ....

8 ugars ....

B

Write the names of these animals.

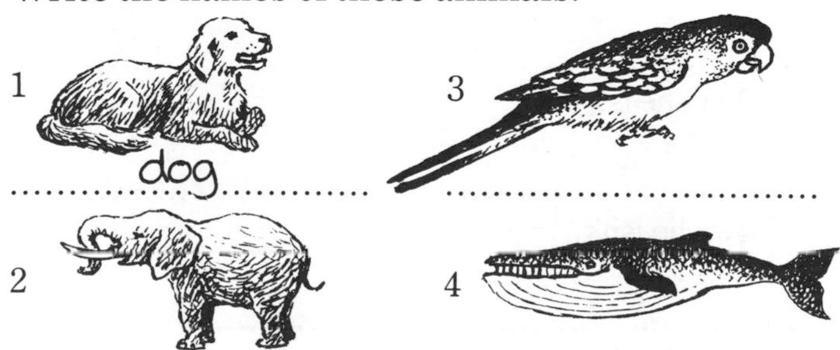

1 dog

2 ....

3 ....

4 ....

5 ....

6 ....

7 ....

8 ....

C

Make words from these letters.
Draw a picture to show you understand.

My drawing

1 raj ....

2 lobw ....

3 slags ....

4 oxb ....

5 ottleb ....

6 nti ....

UNIT 15

A

What do you think Henry is saying? Complete the sentences with *going to*.

1 I'm going to ride this scooter .

2 I ....

3 We ....

4 I ....

5 I ....

6 I ....

7 We're not .... !

B

Use *going to* to write a question for each picture in A. The answer to the question must be true.

■ Example

1 Is Henry going to ride a bicycle ?
No, he isn't.

2 .... ?
Yes, he is.

3 .... ?
No, they aren't.

4 .... ?
Yes, he is.

5 .... ?
Yes, he is.

6 .... ?
No, he isn't.

7 .... ?
No, they're not.

C

You are with a friend when you see these.
What suggestions do you make?
Use *Let's*.

1 Let's have an ice-cream ....

FILM SHOWING NOW
INDIANA JONES and the LAST CRUSADE

2 ....

MADONNA
IN CONCERT
September 7th
8 PM
WEMBLEY STADIUM

3 ....

4 ....

5 ....

ORANGE JUICE
LEMON JUICE

6 ....

D

APRIL
Going on holiday
Going to the cinema
Going to visit the Boss
Going to the dentist

What are you going to do?
Complete these sentences.

1 This evening I'm ....

....

2 Tomorrow I'm ....

....

3 Next Sunday I'm ....

....

4 In August I'm ....

....

5 Next year I'm ....

....

6 At the weekend I'm ....

....

UNIT

16

A

Put in the correct form of *to be*.

This ......is...... a photograph of Henry when he

[1]............ a baby. He [2]............ a happy baby.

In this photograph he [3]............ five. His hair

[4]............ long, black and curly. He [5]............ happy

but fat.

This [6]............ Henry today. His hair [7]............

long and curly and he [8]............ fat. He [9]............ a

happy baby but he [10]............ happy today.

B

Get a photo or draw a picture of you as a baby.

Use these questions to help you write a description.
Ask your family for some of the answers.

How old were you?
Was your hair long/short/curly/straight?
Was your hair light or dark?
Were you fat or thin?
Were you happy?

- Example

In this picture I was ....

My hair ....

....

....

....

C

Olympic Quiz

Are these sentences true or false?
Change the sentences which are false.

1 The Olympic games happen every four years.

True ....

2 The first ancient games were in Athens.

False. They were in Olympia ....

3 There are six Olympic rings.

....

4 The 1988 Olympics were in Tokyo.

....

5 The winner of the marathon in the Rome Olympics was Greek.

....

6 There weren't any women in the first modern Olympics.

....

7 There was prize money in the first modern Olympics.

....

D

Where were they yesterday afternoon?

NICK LEWIS

1 Nick was at school ....

ROXY CINEMA WOODFORD
STALLS
ADMIT ONE
29 October
4.00 pm

2 Henry ....

TAN

3 Shirley and Kate ....

4 Helen ....

5 Nick's mother ....

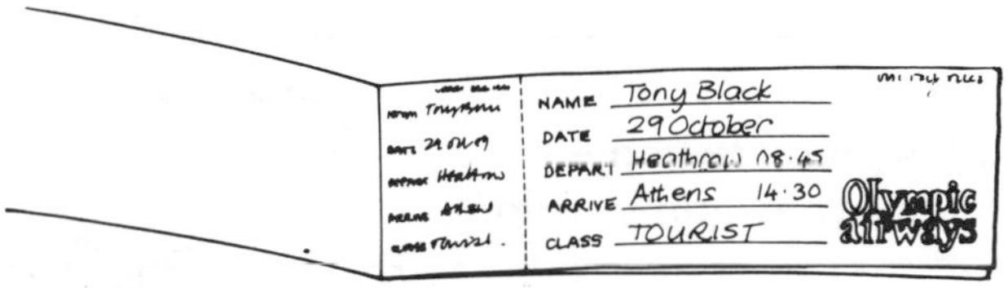

NAME Tony Black
DATE 29 October
DEPART Heathrow 08·45
ARRIVE Athens 14·30
CLASS TOURIST
Olympic airways

6 Tony ....

EXTRA! EXTRA!

A

Complete the words in this conversation.

Helen Hello! C _ _ I speak to Nick, please?

Nick Speaking.

Helen It's Helen here. What a _ _ y _ _ d _ _ _ _ this evening?

Nick Nothing, I haven't g _ _ any p _ _ _ _ _ .

Helen S _ _ _ _ w _ go to the cinema?

Nick W _ _ _' _ on?

Helen A cowboy f _ _ _ . Clint Westwood is in it.

Nick G _ _ _ _ idea! L _ _' _ g _ .

Helen Come to my house a _ 6.30.

Nick Sure! See you then. B _ _ !

Helen Goodbye!

B

What is going to happen?
What are they going to do?

1 He is going to play the piano .

2 They ....

3 She ....

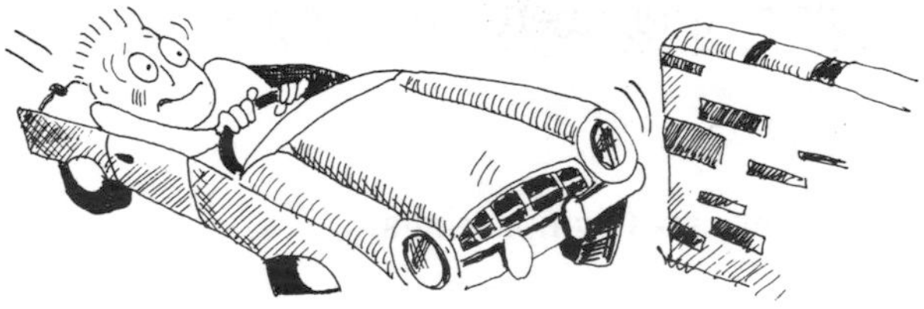

4 He ....

5 He ....

6 She ....

7 She ....

WORDPOWER

A

What are they going to do?
Use the table to make six sentences about the picture.

He She	is going to	fly ride drive	a horse. a car. a bus. a plane. a balloon. a motor cycle.

1 ....

2 ....

3 ....

4 ....

5 ....

6 ....

■ Example

She is going to fly a plane .

B

Match the words in A to their opposites in B.

A	B
happy	women
late	sad
fat	short
professional	straight
tall	thin
curly	early
men	amateur

C

How many words can you make from the letters in this word?

DEFINITELY

■ Example

tin

....

....

....

....

....

....

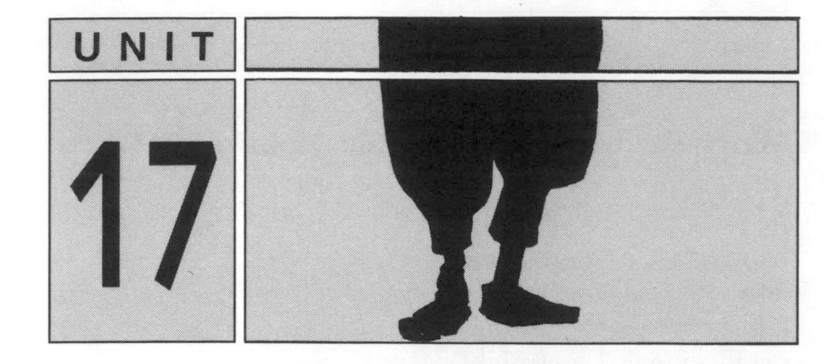

A

Use the simple past of these verbs to complete Nick's letter.

be *cook* *iron* *hate* *wash up*
tidy *do*

Dear Helen,

Yesterday [1]............ Mum's birthday. She [2]............ nothing! My sister [3]............ the meals and I [4]............ .... afterwards! ! My father [5]............ his shirts and I [6]............ my room! ! I [7]............ doing my Mum's job!

My sister doesn't want to be a housewife. I think she's right. Don't you?

Best wishes,

Nick

B

Match the verbs in column A with their past tense form in column B.

A	B
be	took
do	watched
have	drank
buy	did
begin	ate
drink	dusted
sign	played
eat	emptied
make	bought
put	made
empty	began
dust	tidied
tidy	had
take	put
watch	was
play	signed

C

Henry went to Italy for his holiday. What did he do?

1 have / pizza / restaurant

He had a pizza in a restaurant .

2 make / pasta

He ....

3 take / photographs

He ....

4 go to / beach

He ....

5 drink / Italian wine

He ....

6 get up / late

He ....

7 buy / fruit / market

He ....

D

Make six sentences about the things you did last Sunday.

1 ....

2 ....

3 ....

4 ....

5 ....

6 ....

E

Word square

Circle the simple past tense of six verbs.

S	T	E	W	B	T
C	A	M	E	E	R
A	K	W	N	G	I
R	E	N	T	A	E
E	D	R	A	N	D
T	H	R	E	W	L

Make six sentences. Use each verb once.

■ Example

Peter threw the keys in the dustbin .

1 ....

2 ....

3 ....

4 ....

5 ....

6 ....

UNIT 18

A

Last year Nick went on holiday with his Aunt Mabel. Complete his letter with the negative form of the verbs in brackets.

Dear Alex,

I'm back from my holiday with Aunt Mabel. It was terrible! Aunt Mabel .... (want) to go to the beach. She wanted to visit museums all the time! I hated that. There .... (be) any interesting things to look at.

The weather .... (be) very good either. The sun .... (shine) and it rained a lot. I .... (see) any of my friends. There were two cinemas but I .... (have) any money and Aunt Mabel .... (give) me any! It .... (be) a very good holiday and I'm pleased to be home.

See you soon.

Nick

B

Use five of these to make true sentences about what you didn't do yesterday.

■ Example

I didn't play basketball.

1 ....

2 ....

3 ....

4 ....

5 ....

C

Write a request for each picture.

■ Example

1 *bring me / case*

Would you bring me the case, please?

2 open / window

.... ?

3 help me with / this

.... ?

4 pass me / water

.... ?

5 close / door

.... ?

6 come / here

.... ?

D

Tony had a lot of jobs last weekend. Write down the things he did and didn't do.

Things to do

wash the car ✓
tidy the house
water the plants ✓
write a letter to Shirley
phone Mum
clean the kitchen ✓
do the ironing
go to the supermarket
make bread ✓

■ Examples

He washed the car.

He didn't tidy the house.

1 ....

2 ....

3 ....

4 ....

5 ....

6 ....

7 ....

EXTRA! EXTRA!

A

Put the verbs in the simple past tense.

My name is Graham. Last week I ...was... (be) on 'Try it!' For three days I .... (be) a fire-officer.

We .... (learn) how to put out fires.

We .... (have) lessons in first aid and I .... (take) an exam. In the exam I .... (kiss) a plastic dummy.

I .... (learn) to use the emergency ladder and I .... (climb) to the top. I .... (feel) a little frightened.

It .... (be) good. I .... (like) being a fire-officer.

B

Write down the things that you think Henry didn't do yesterday.

1 He didn't wash the dishes .

2 ....

3 ....

4 ....

RABBIT

5 ....

C

Write the past tense of these verbs.

1 learn ....
2 spend ....
3 feel ....
4 make ....
5 swim ....
6 put ....
7 do ....
8 get ....
9 go ....

WORDPOWER

A

Write down the name of

1 your favourite pop star

....

2 your favourite band

....

3 a record

....

4 a record shop

....

B

Write the names.

1 ....

2 ....

3 ....

4 ....

5 ....

6 ....

7 ....

C

Write in the verbs for these definitions.

■ Example

eat............

Put food in your mouth and swallow.

Henry and Den ...eat... *a lot.*

1 ....

Take water, milk, coffee, etc. through the mouth.

Babies .... *milk.*

2 ....

Clean dishes, plates, etc. with water.

We .... *after breakfast.*

3 ....

Make food ready to eat.

My mother .... *lunch.*

4 ....

Put things in the right place.

I .... *my room.*

5 ....

Look at someone or something for some time.

The children .... *TV.*

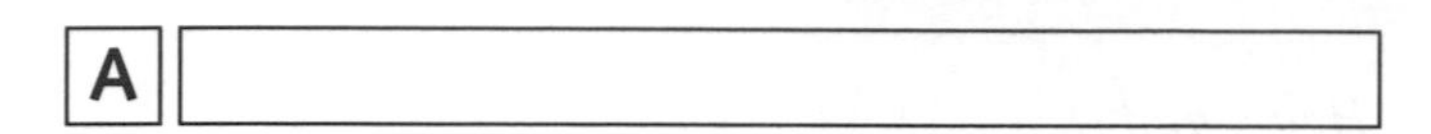

Look at these pictures and make the questions.

1 When / hurt / hand?

When did you hurt your hand ?

2 How / break / leg?

How .... ?

3 When / cut / finger?

When .... ?

4 How / crack / head?

How .... ?

5 How / break / arm?

How .... ?

6 When / burn / hand?

When .... ?

B

You are the person in the pictures in A. Answer the questions in A. Use the pictures below to help you.

1 When I was ten .

2 ....

3 ....

4 ....

5 ....

6 ....

C

Use the simple past tense to complete this postcard.

Dear Nick,

I .... (arrive) at the *WOW* camp on Thursday.

The next day I .... (go) for a ride on a horse. I .... (fall) off and .... (break) my leg. That hurt!! They .... (take) me to hospital. I .... (come) home yesterday and the good thing is that I can't go to school.

Please telephone me soon.

Alex

D

Who invented these?
Write five quiz questions about inventions.

(The answers are at the bottom of the page).

■ Example

Who invented the television?

Sandwich: The Earl of Sandwich
Windsurfer: Peter Chilvers
Telephone:Alexander Graham Bell
Ballpoint pen: Lasalo Biro
Radio: Marconi
Television: John Logie Baird

UNIT 20

A

Look at the picture and complete the text. Use the simple past.

1 Shirley ....took.... some large sheets of newspaper.

2 She .... the newspaper on the table.

3 She made sure the long edge .... along the edge of the table.

4 She .... a ruler and put it under the newspaper.

5 She .... the paper flat.

6 Nick .... the ruler hard.

7 The ruler ....

B

Follow the instructions in the pictures. Write down what happened.

1 Get in this position.

Try to jump forwards. What happened?

....

Try to jump backwards. What happened?

....

2 Now do this.

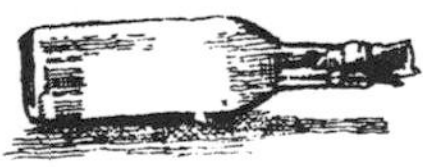

Place an empty bottle on its side.

Put some paper in the neck.

Try to blow the paper into the bottle.

What happened?

....

....

C

Write an appropriate goodbye for each picture.

1 Have a good holiday .

2 Goodnight! Nice ....

3 Bye! Have ....

4 Have ....

5 Goodnight! Hope ....

D

Match the words in column A with the words in column B.

	A		B
1	He didn't eat because	a	he wasn't hungry.
2	I didn't go to school because	b	she didn't have any money.
3	She didn't go to the cinema because	c	the dog ate my textbook.
4	Tony didn't tidy his room because	d	the bus was late.
5	I was late for school because	e	he didn't have time.
6	I didn't do my homework because	f	I broke my leg.

■ Example

He didn't eat because he wasn't hungry.

EXTRA! EXTRA!

A

Complete the interviewer's questions.

1

.... your hand? I put it through the window.

.... you then? I was six.

.... to hospital? Yes.

.... took you? My mother and father did.

2

.... your leg? I broke it in Switzerland.

.... happened? I fell off my skis.

.... happen? When I was twelve.

3

.... that scar? I cut my hand.

.... cut it with? With a knife.

.... do it? In the kitchen.

B

Use the pictures to write a simple story.

C

Write a postcard to a friend.
Tell her/him about your holiday plans.

Dear

I'm writing to you about my holiday plans.

This summer ....

....

....

....

....

What are you doing?

....

D

Write down four things you're going to do to learn English in the holiday.

■ Example

I'm going to read English books.

1 ....

2 ....

3 ....

4 ....

WORDPOWER

A

Crossword

The answers are the base forms of these past tense forms.

Across
1 cut
3 asked
4 kicked
6 hurt
7 stepped
9 met

Down
1 cracked
2 took
4 kept
5 bet
6 hit
7 saw
8 put

B

Complete the sentences with the simple past tense of the correct verb.

■ Example

I fell down a hole ....

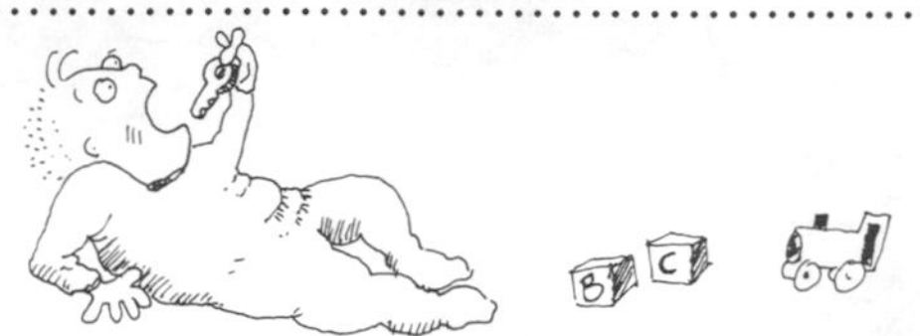

1 I .... a key.

2 I .... in the sea.

3 I .... my arm.

4 I .... my thumb with a knife.

5 I .... my hair.

C

Write the names of these things.

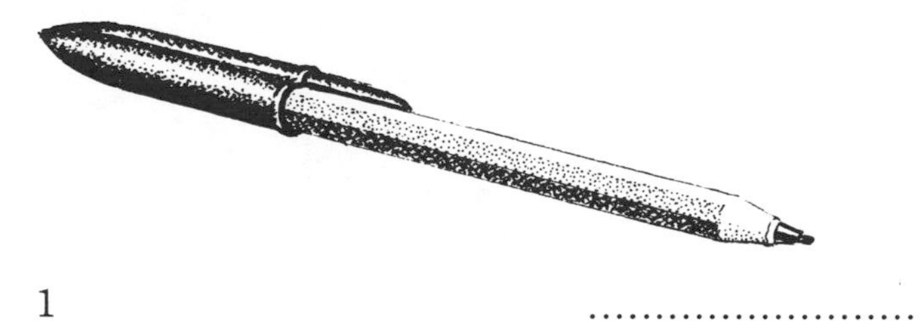

1 ....

2 ....

3 ....

4 ....

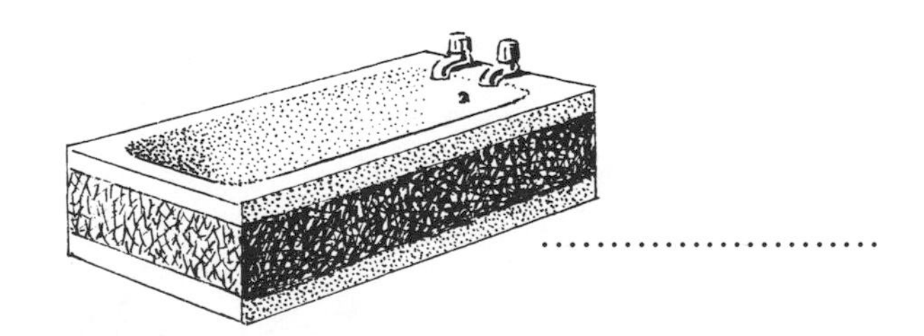

5 ....

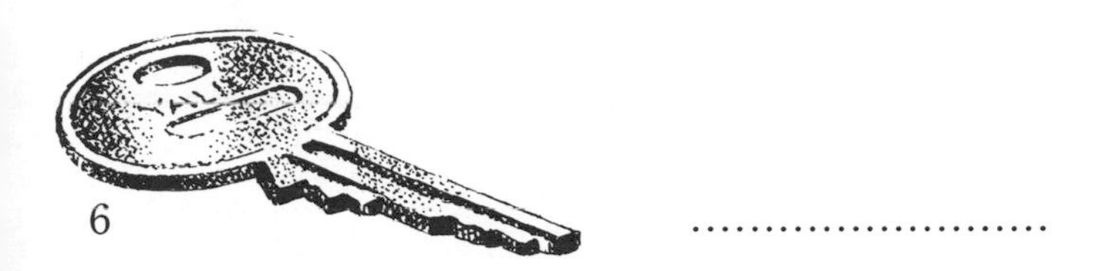

6 ....

D

Match the examples a–c with the correct definitions 1–3.

a The *last* show was *last* night.
b His hair is *long*. How *long* are your holidays?
c Make sure the table is *smooth* (adj).

1

> *adj.* **1** from one end to the other: *The snake is a metre* . **2** from beginning to end: *Our holidays are two weeks* . **3** far from one end to the other: *hair*. **4** lasting a lot of time: *a film.*

2

> *adj.* **1** not rough; flat: *A baby has a skin.* **2** that does not shake or bump you; gentle: *a ride.* **3** not difficult; with no problems: *a meeting.*

3

> *adj.* **1** at the end, after all others: *December is the month in the year.* **2** coming just before the present: *It's June now, so month was May.* **3** only one left: *This is your chance.*

Oxford University Press
Walton Street, Oxford OX2 6DP

Oxford New York
Athens Auckland Bangkok Bombay
Calcutta Cape Town Dar es Salaam Delhi
Florence Hong Kong Istanbul Karachi
Kuala Lumpur Madras Madrid Melbourne
Mexico City Nairobi Paris Singapore
Taipei Tokyo Toronto

and associated companies in
Berlin Ibadan

OXFORD AND OXFORD ENGLISH
are trade marks of Oxford University Press

ISBN 0 19 432454 0
© Oxford University Press 1990
First published 1990
Eighth impression 1994

Set by Pentacor PLC, High Wycombe

Printed in Malta by Interprint Limited

No unauthorized photocopying

All rights reserved. No part of this publication may be reproduced, stored in a retrieval system, or transmitted, in any form or by any means, electronic, mechanical, photocopying, recording, or otherwise, without the prior written permission of Oxford University Press.

This book is sold subject to the condition that it shall not, by way of trade or otherwise, be lent, re-sold, hired out, or otherwise circulated without the publisher's prior consent in any form of binding or cover other than that in which it is published and without a similar condition including this condition being imposed on the subsequent purchaser.

Acknowledgements

Illustrations by: Robina Green; JoneSewell & Associates; Sîan Leetham; Joseph McEwan; Joanna Quinn

Cover illustration by: Terry Kennett